the 365 days of peace
journal

jessica kantrowitz

365 Days of Peace
Benedictions to End Your Day in Gentleness and
Hope

Cover art by Kozakura on Fiverr

peace to...

~

peace to all who enter here
peace to the writers and the scribblers
peace to the thinkers and the over-thinkers
peace to those who process through writing
and to those who process through talking but
don't have anyone to talk to
right now
peace to those afraid of blank pages
who worry their words won't make sense
or look pretty
these pages were made for you
they are waiting for your words
don't be afraid

~

peace to...

peace to...

peace to...

peace to...

peace to...

peace to...

peace to...

peace to...

peace to...

peace to...

peace to...

peace to...

peace to...

peace to...

peace to...

peace to...

peace to...

peace to...

peace to...

peace to...

peace to...

peace to...

peace to...

peace to...

peace to...

peace to...

peace to...

peace to...

peace to...

peace to...

peace to...

peace to...

peace to...

peace to...

peace to...

peace to...

peace to . . .

peace to...

peace to...

peace to...

peace to...

peace to...

peace to...

peace to...

peace to...

peace to...

peace to...

peace to...

peace to...

peace to...

peace to...

peace to...

peace to...

peace to...

peace to...

peace to...

peace to...

peace to...

peace to...

peace to...

peace to...

peace to...

peace to...

~

peace to those who have lingered here
writing your thoughts
writing your ideas
writing your dreams
your fears and your prayers
your to-do lists and your lists of what you've
done
peace to the things you've yet to do
which you will write in a
new journal
thank you for spending some time in this one

go in peace

~

Printed in Great Britain
by Amazon